Ghosts and Goblins and Freaks and Ghouls

Music Mentor

JERALD SIMON

musicmotivation.com

Cool music that excites, entertains, and educates!

Learn how to play piano the FUN way!
The Apprentice Stage - The Maestro Stage - The Virtuoso Stage

Music Motivation® books are designed to provide students with music instruction that will enable them to improve and increase their successes in the field of music. It is also intended to enhance appreciation and understanding of various styles of music from classical to jazz, blues, rock, popular, new age, hymns, and more. The author and publisher disclaim any liability or accountability for the misuse of this material as it was intended by the author.

To the wonderful piano teachers, piano students and parent
piano students who are using my music. Thank you. I very m
appreciate your continued encouragement and support. It pus
me forward. I hope you enjoy "Ghosts and Goblins and Fre
and Ghouls". These fun, scary piano solos were composed v
teenagers in mind - especially teenage boys, and are also grea
student savers. These are very fun performance pieces any stud
would want to play and perform. Minus tracks can be used as v
You will hear the accompaniment music at three speeds:

(1) Performance Speed with Piano, (2) Performance Speed -
Piano, and (3) Practice Speed - No Piano.

Your Music Mentor Jerald Sir

This book is dedicated to the many website
subscribers who follow my blog and watch
my videos on my YouTube page (youtube.
com/jeraldsimon)Also, for my wife, Suzanne
(Zanny), my sweet daughter, Summer, and
my two sons, Preston, and Matthew.

The family portrait on the back cover was shot by
Wendy Santiano. Visit her website at:

http://www.wendysantiano.com or
https://www.facebook.com/wsantianoauthor

The front and background image is from the website:
http://www.istockphoto.com -
Copyright ©iStock.com/najin

CONNECT with Jerald

http://musicmotivation.com/jeraldsimon
https://facebook.com/jeraldsimon
http://youtube.com/jeraldsimon
http://linkedin.com/in/jeraldsimon
http://pinterest.com/jeraldsimon
https://twitter.com/jeraldsimon
http://cdbaby.com/artist/jeraldsimon
http://instagram.com/jeraldsimon
jeraldsimon@musicmotivation.com

CONTACT Music Motivation®

Music Motivation®
Cool music that excites, entertains, and educates!™

Music Motivation®
P.O. Box 1000
Kaysville, UT 84037-1000
http://musicmotivation.com
https://facebook.com/musicmotivation
https://twitter.com/musicmotivation
info@musicmotivation.com

First Printing 2015 - Printed in the United States of America - 10 9 8 7 6 5 4 3 2 1 - Simon, Jerald - Music Motivation® - Ghosts and Goblins and Freaks and
Ghouls- $16.95 US/ $18.95 Canada - Soft cover spiral bound book - ISBN-13: 978-0-9980785-0-2 - MM00001021

Music Motivation® is a registered ® trademark

Welcome to
"Ghosts and Goblins and Freaks and Ghouls"
by JERALD SIMON

Piano teachers, piano students, and parents of piano students continually search for fun and exciting piano music their students can't wait to play.

The search is over with Music Motivation® and the music composed by Jerald Simon!

Jerald Simon is a popular pianist, composer, author, and performer/motivational speaker, who composes fun piano music that piano students love playing and performing for family and friends. Simon is well-known for his **COOL SONGS Series** (https://www.musicmotivation.com/coolsongs) which features over 200 of his fun, original piano music - most of which include accompaniment MP3 minus tracks to help piano students learn to play the piano the fun way. He is also wellknown for his **Essential Piano Exercises Series** (https://www.essentialpianoexercises.com/pdf/series), as well as his popular Music Motivation® website and company (https://www.musicmotivation.com/).

In "Ghosts and Goblins and Freaks and Ghouls," Simon has composed 10 new original intermediate - advanced level piano solos that are scary Halloween pieces. You can listen to any of these pieces on any streaming site (e.g. Spotify, iTunes, Amazon, etc.). You can also watch the music videos on Jerald's YouTube channel (YouTube.com/jeraldsimon).

I can't wait to have you play these fun and scary sounding piano solos. You can purchase the PDF book on my website and gain access to individual pre-recorded piano lessons where I demonstrate how to play each of these scary piano solos. You will also have access to the accompanying MP3 minus tracks.

I'd like to introduce myself and tell you more about myself and why I love composing fun music to help motivate teens and adults.

My name is Jerald Simon. First and foremost, I am a husband to my beautiful wife, Zanny (her name is Suzanne - but anyone who knows her calls her Zanny), and a father to my three wonderful children, Summer, Preston, and Matthew. They are wonderful, and everything I do is for them. God and family always comes first in my life!

I am the founder of **Music Motivation®** (musicmotivation.com), and the creator of the Cool Songs Series (musicmotivation.com/coolsongs), and the Essential Piano Exercises Series/Course (essentialpianoexercises.com). I teach weekly online group piano lessons to students all over the world (essentialpianolessons.com). I have a YouTube channel (youtube.com/jeraldsimon), and I love learning everything I can, and want to help myself and others do our best and live our best life.

This is my Purpose and Mission in life:

"My purpose and mission in life is to motivate myself and others through my music and writing, to help others find their purpose and mission in life, and to teach values that encourage everyone everywhere to do and be their best." – Jerald Simon

Be sure to check out Jerald's **BEST-SELLING** piano book series: **Essential Piano Exercises Every Piano Player Should Know.** There are currently four books in the series. Other books in this series will soon be available as well (e.g. **Essential Pop Piano Exercises Every Piano Player Should Know, Essential Rock Piano Exercises Every Piano Player Should Know, 100 Chord Progressions Every Piano Player Should Know, 100 Improvised Licks Every Piano Player Should Know,** and so forth).

The four books currently in the series are:

"100 Left Hand Patterns Every Piano Player Should Know," "Essential Piano Exercises Every Piano Player Should Know," "Essential Jazz Piano Exercises Every Piano Player Should Know," and **"Essential New Age Piano Exercises Every Piano Player Should Know."**

You can learn more about these books from the Essential Piano Exercises Series and learn more about the course which you can sign up for at https://www.essentialpianoexercises.com/. The Essential Piano Exercises Series teaches fun exercises through original music I have composed.

A message from Jerald to piano students and parents:

If you come to piano lessons each week and walk away only having learned about music notation, rhythm, and dots on a page, then I have failed as a Music Mentor. Life lessons are just as important, if not more important than music lessons. I would rather have you learn more about goal setting and achieving, character, dedication, and personal improvement. To have you learn to love music, appreciate it, and play it, is a wonderful byproduct you will have for the rest of your life - a talent that will enrich your life and the lives of others. To become a better musician is wonderful and important, but to become a better person is more important.

As a Music Mentor I want to mentor students to be the very best they can be. If you choose not to practice, you essentially choose not to improve. This is true in any area of life. Everyone has the same amount of time allotted to them. What you choose to do with your time, and where you spend your time, has little to do with the activities being done and more to do with the value attached to each activity.

I believe it's important to be well-rounded and have many diverse interests. I want students to enjoy music, to learn to be creative and understand how to express themselves musically - either by creating music of their own, or interpreting the music of others - by arranging and improvising well known music. In addition, I encourage students to play sports, dance, sing, draw, read, and develop all of their talents. I want them to be more than musicians, I want them to learn to become well-rounded individuals.

Above all, I want everyone to continually improve and do their best. I encourage everyone to set goals, dream big, and be the best they can be in whatever they choose to do. Life is full of wonderful choices. Choose the best out of life and learn as much as you can from everyone everywhere. I prefer being called a Music Mentor because I want to mentor others and help them to live their dreams.

Your life is your musical symphony. Make it a masterpiece!

Music Mentor

JERALD SIMON

Learn about my three stages of music success from my **Music Mentorship Map** below -
e **Apprentice Stage**, **The Maestro Stage**, and **The Virtuoso Stage** - https://www.essentialpianolessons.com

The *Music Motivation*® Mentorship Map (for piano students)
by Music Mentor™ Jerald Simon

Music Motivation®
musicmotivation.com

	Apprentice for 1ˢᵗ & 2ⁿᵈ year students	Maestro for 2ⁿᵈ - 4ᵗʰ year students	Virtuoso for 3ʳᵈ year students and above
Repertoire In addition to the books listed to the right, students can sign up to receive the weekly "Cool Song" and "Cool Exercise" composed by Jerald Simon every week. Visit musicmotivation.com/musicsubscription to learn more and sign up!	**Music Motivation® Book(s)** What Every Pianist Should Know (Free PDF) Essential Piano Exercises (section 1) Cool Songs for Cool Kids (pre-primer level) Cool Songs for Cool Kids (primer level) Cool Songs for Cool Kids (book 1) The Pentascale Pop Star (books 1 and 2) Songs in Pentascale position: Classical, Jazz, Blues, Popular, Students Choice, Personal Composition (in pentascale position - 5 note piano solo) etc.	**Music Motivation® Book(s)** Essential Piano Exercises (section 2) An Introduction to Scales and Modes Cool Songs for Cool Kids (book 2) Cool Songs for Cool Kids (book 3) Variations on Mary Had a Little Lamb Twinkle Those Stars, Jazzed about Christmas, Jazzed about 4th of July Baroque, Romantic, Classical, Jazz, Blues, Popular, New Age, Student's Choice, Personal Composition.	**Music Motivation® Book(s)** Essential Piano Exercises (section 3) Cool Songs that ROCK! (books 1 & 2) Triumphant, Sea Fever, Sweet Melancholy, The Dawn of a New Age, Sweet Modality, Jazzed about Jazz, Jazzed about Classical Music, Jingle Those Bells, Cinematic Solos, Hymn Arranging Baroque, Romantic, Classical, Jazz, Blues, Popular, New Age, Contemporary, Broadway Show Tunes, Standards, Student's Choice, Personal Composition
Music Terminology	Piano (*p*), Forte (*f*) Mezzo Piano (*mp*) Mezzo Forte (*mf*) Pianissimo (*pp*) Fortissimo (*ff*) *Music Motivation® 1ˢᵗ Year Terminology*	Tempo Markings Dynamic Markings Parts of the Piano Styles and Genres of Music *Music Motivation® 2ⁿᵈ Year Terminology*	Pocket Music Dictionary (2 - 3 years) Harvard Dictionary of Music (4 + years) Parts/History of the Piano Music Composers (Weekly Biographies) *Music Motivation® 3ʳᵈ Year Terminology*
Key Signatures	C, G, D, A, F, B♭, E♭ & A♭ (Major) A, E, B, F♯, D, G, C & F (Minor) Begin learning all major key signatures	Circle of 5ths/Circle of 4ths <u>All</u> Major and Minor key signatures (Identify each key and name the sharps and flats)	Spiral of Fifths, Chord Progressions within Key Signatures. Modulating from one Key Signature to another.
Music Notation	Names and Positions of notes on the staff (both hands - Treble and Bass Clefs)	Names and Positions of notes above and below the staff (both hands)	History of Music Notation (the development of notation), Monks & Music, Gregorian Chants, Music changes over the years and how music has changed. Learn **Finale** and **Logic Pro** (notate your music)
Rhythms	Whole notes/rests (say it and play it - count out loud) Half notes/rests (say it and play it - count out loud) Quarter notes/rests (say it and play it - count out loud) Eighth notes/rests (say it and play it - count out loud)	Sixteenth notes/rests (say it and play it - count out loud) Thirty-second notes/rests (say it and play it - count out loud) Sixty-fourth notes/rests (say it and play it - count out loud)	One-hundred-twenty-eighth notes/rests For more on rhythm, I recommend: "Rhythmic Training"by Robert Starer and "Logical Approach to Rhythmic Notation" (books 1 & 2) by Phil Perkins
Intervals	1ˢᵗ, 2ⁿᵈ, 3ʳᵈ, 4ᵗʰ, 5ᵗʰ, 6ᵗʰ, 7ᵗʰ, 8ᵗʰ, and 9ᵗʰ intervals (key of C, G, D, F, B♭, and E♭). Harmonic and Melodic intervals (key of C, G, D, A, E, and B)	<u>All</u> Perfect, Major, Minor, Augmented, and Diminished intervals (in every key) <u>All</u> Harmonic and Melodic intervals Explain the intervals used to create major, minor, diminished, and augmented chords?	9ᵗʰ, 11ᵗʰ, and 13ᵗʰ intervals Analyze music (Hymns and Classical) to identify intervals used in each measure. Identify/Name intervals used in chords.
Scales	<u>All</u> Major Pentascales (5 finger scale) <u>All</u> Minor Pentascales (5 finger scale) <u>All</u> Diminished Pentascales (5 finger scale) C Major Scale (1 octave) A min. Scale (1 oct.) (Do, Re, Mi, Fa, Sol, La, Ti, Do) (solfege) All Major and Natural Minor Scales - 1 octave	<u>All</u> Major Scales (Every Key 1 - 2 octaves) <u>All</u> Minor Scales (Every Key 1 - 2 octaves) (natural, harmonic, and melodic minor scales) (Do, Di, Re, Ri, Mi, Fa, Fi, Sol, Si, La, Li, Ti, Do) (solfege - chromatic)	<u>All</u> Major Scales (Every Key 3 - 5 Octaves) <u>All</u> Minor Scales (Every Key 3 - 5 Octaves) <u>All</u> Blues Scales (major and minor) Cultural Scales (25 + scales)
Modes	Ionian/Aeolian (C/A, G/E, D/B, A/F♯)	<u>All</u> Modes (I, D, P, L, M, A, L) <u>All</u> keys	Modulating with the Modes (Dorian to Dorian)
Chords	<u>All</u> Major Chords, <u>All</u> Minor Chords, <u>All</u> Diminished Chords, C Sus 2, C Sus 4, C+ (Aug.), C 6ᵗʰ, C minor 6ᵗʰ, C 7ᵗʰ, C Maj. 7ᵗʰ, C minor Major 7ᵗʰ, A min., A Sus 2, A Sus 4,	<u>All</u> Major, Minor, Diminished, Augmented, Sus 2, Sus 4, Sixth, Minor Sixth, Dominant 7ᵗʰ and Major 7ᵗʰ Chords	Review <u>All</u> Chords from 1ˢᵗ and 2ⁿᵈ year experiences <u>All</u> 7ᵗʰ, 9ᵗʰ, 11ᵗʰ, and 13ᵗʰ chords inversions and voicings.
Arpeggios	Same chords as above (1 - 2 octaves)	Same chords as above (3 - 4 octaves)	Same chords as above (4 + octaves)
Inversions	Same chords as above (1 - 2 octaves)	Same chords as above (3 - 4 octaves)	Same chords as above (4 + octaves)
Technique (other)	Schmitt Preparatory Exercises, (Hanon)	Wieck, Hanon, Bach (well tempered clavier)	Bertini-Germer, Czerny, I. Philipp
Sight Reading	Key of C Major and G Major	Key of C, G, D, A, E, F, B♭, E♭, A♭, D♭	<u>All</u> Key Signatures, Hymns, Classical
Ear Training	Major versus Minor sounds (chords/intervals)	C, D, E, F, G, A, B, and intervals	Key Signatures and Chords, Play w/ IPod
Music History	The origins of the Piano Forte	Baroque, Classical, Jazz, Blues	Students choice - <u>All</u> genres, Composers
Improvisation	Mary Had a Little Lamb, Twinkle, Twinkle...	Blues Pentascale, Barrelhouse Blues	Classical, New Age, Jazz, Blues, etc. Play w/ IPod
Composition	5 note melody (both hands - key of C and G)	One - Two Page Song (include key change)	Lyrical, Classical, New Age, Jazz, etc.

The books from the Music Motivation® Series by Jerald Simon are not method books, and are not intentionally created to be used as such (although some piano teachers use them as such). Jerald simply creates fun, cool piano music to motivate piano students to play the piano and teach them music theory - the FUN way!

5

In the example below, play the Major, minor, and diminshed chords. These three chords are shown for C Major, C minor, C diminished, F Major, F minor, F diminished, and G Major, G minor, and G diminished.

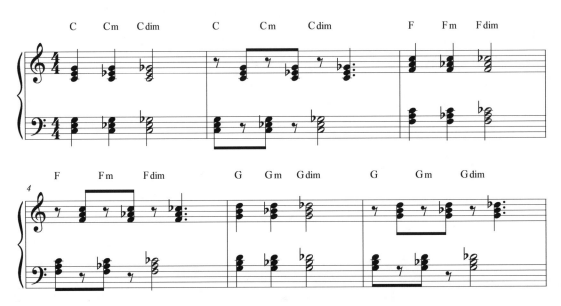

Try this in all keys as well. These chords have a very scary sound and are used throughout this book.

Now play the chromatic pentascale exercise below. Look at the fingering provided. Yes, that is how I want you to play this exercise. Try it. It's a little tricky, especially if you have very large hands, but try it.

Dracula's Dance

This fun "cool song" was created to teach broken chords (G major, G minor, F minor, and C minor).

Watch the YouTube video of Jerald playing this by visiting his YouTube page: youtube.com/jeraldsimon. It is one of the "Cool Songs" videos under the "Ghosts and Goblins and Freaks and Ghouls by Jerald Simon" playlist. You may also type in "Dracula's Dance by Jerald Simon" in the YouTube search box to find the video as well.

How would Count Dracula play this?
Is he really even a "COUNT" at all?
Can you "COUNT" the rhythm? Good Questions!?

JERALD SIMON

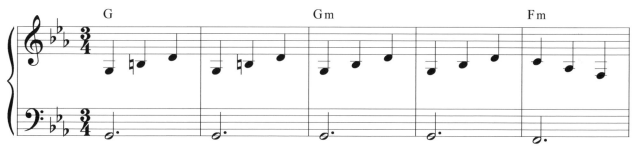

Students can write in their own dynamics!

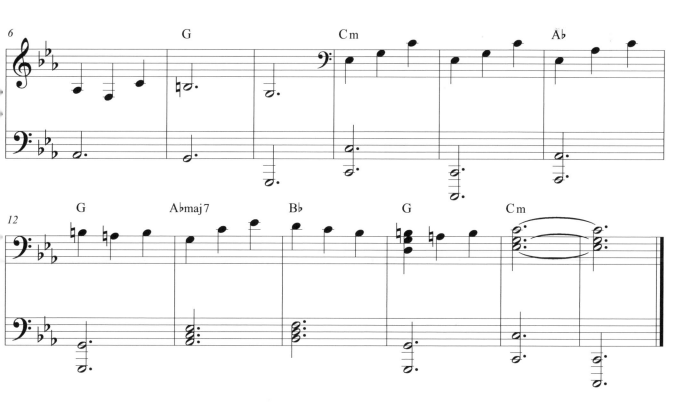

Cool Exercise

This fun "cool exercise" was created to teach the G Major, G minor, and F minor pentascales. The right hand also plays harmonic third intervals starting in measure five. HAVE FUN!

Watch the YouTube video of Jerald playing this by visiting his YouTube page: youtube.com/jeraldsimon. It is one of the "Cool Exercises" videos under the "Ghosts and Goblins and Freaks and Ghouls by Jerald Simon" playlist. You may also type in "Dracula's Dance by Jerald Simon" in the YouTube search box to find the video as well.

JERALD SIMON

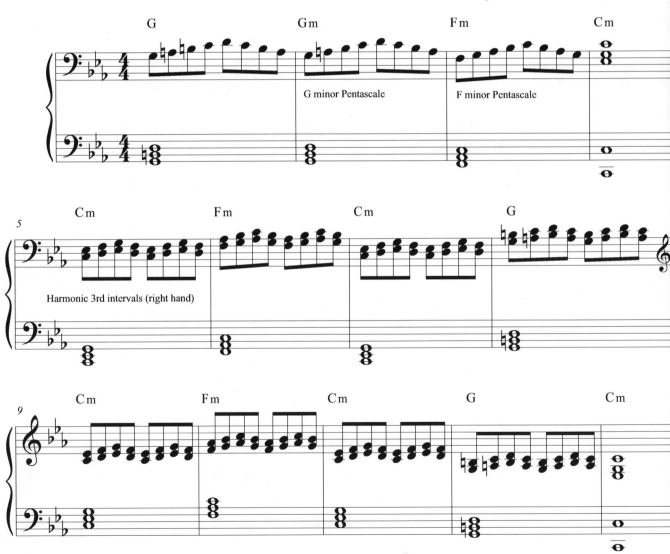

Cool Exercise

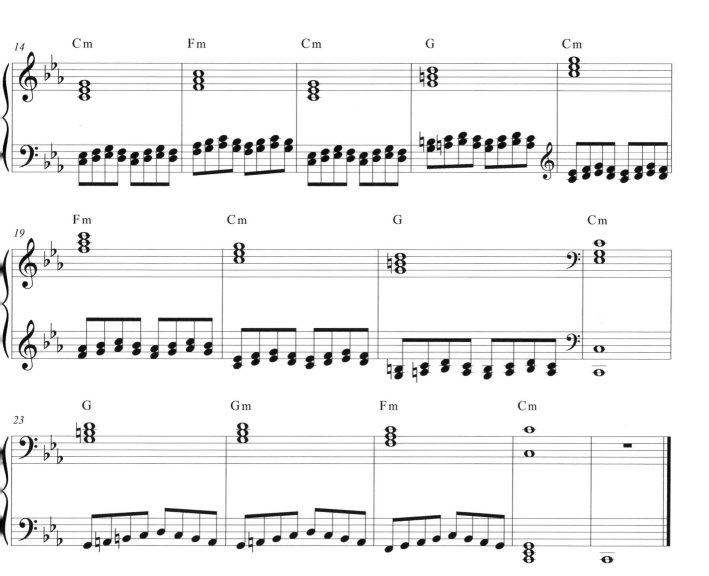

The Dragon's Den of Doom

Skill - Left hand ostinato pattern - Key of D minor, Right Hand crossing over Left Hand

Watch the YouTube video of Jerald playing this by visiting his YouTube page: youtube.com/jeraldsimon. It is one of the "Cool Songs" videos under the "Ghosts and Goblins and Freaks and Ghouls by Jerald Simon" playlist. You may also type in "The Dragon's Den of Doom by Jerald Simon" in the YouTube search box to find the video as well.

Watch Out - it's Behind You! (M.M. ♩ = c. 130)

JERALD SIMON

THE DRAGON'S DEN OF DOOM

WHEN SHARKS ATTACK!

This fun "cool song" was created to teach a half step interval (e.g. E to F) to piano students and to help them with a steady quarter note in the left hand (until measure 29) while the right hand plays eighth notes "on beat" and "off beat" with the eighth rests (in measure 9). HAVE FUN!

Watch the YouTube video of Jerald playing this by visiting his YouTube page: youtube.com/jeraldsimon. It is one of the "Cool Songs" videos under the "Ghosts and Goblins and Freaks and Ghouls by Jerald Simon" playlist. You may also type in "When Sharks Attack! by Jerald Simon" in the YouTube search box to find the video as well.

JERALD SIMON

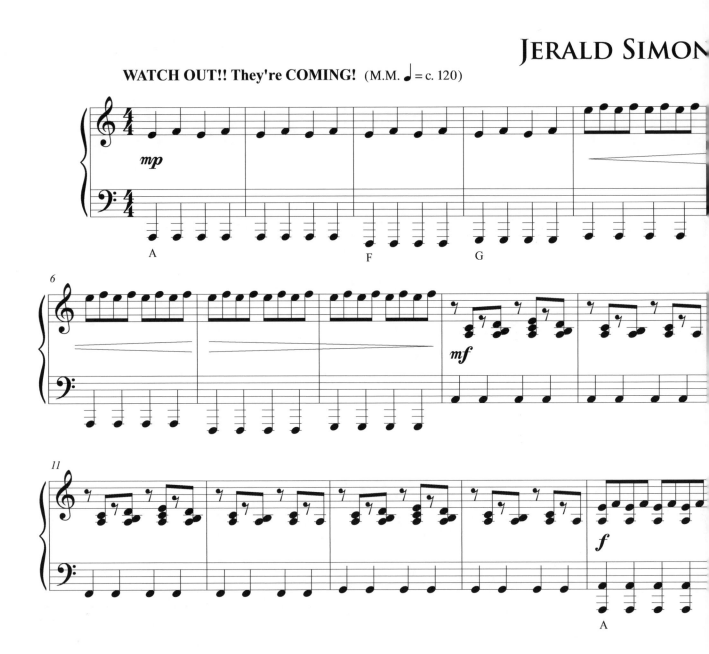

When Sharks Attack!

Goblin Getaway

Titled by Jarom Young

This fun "cool song" was created to show a practical application of half steps crossing over each other (e.g. measure 2), and also to help students watch the staccato. They also practice an octave interval (with the left hand) whil playing staccatos with the right hand (e.g. measure 30). HAVE FUN!

Watch the YouTube video of Jerald playing this by visiting his YouTube page: youtube.com/jeraldsimon. It is one of the "Cool Songs" videos under the "Ghosts and Goblins and Freaks and Ghouls by Jerald Simon" playlist. You may also type in "Goblin Getaway by Jerald Simon" in the YouTube search box to find the video as well.

JERALD SIMON

Cautiously - Don't let em get away! (M.M. ♩ = c. 120)

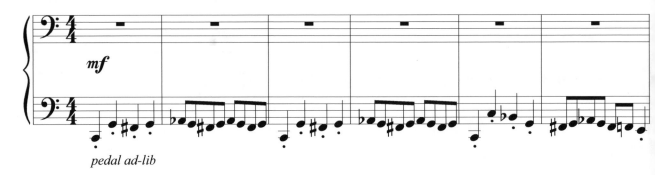

Goblin Getaway

C

DARKNESS

Skill - Students learn the a perfect fifth interval with the left hand, and a chromatic scale with the right hand.

JERALD SIMON

DARKNESS

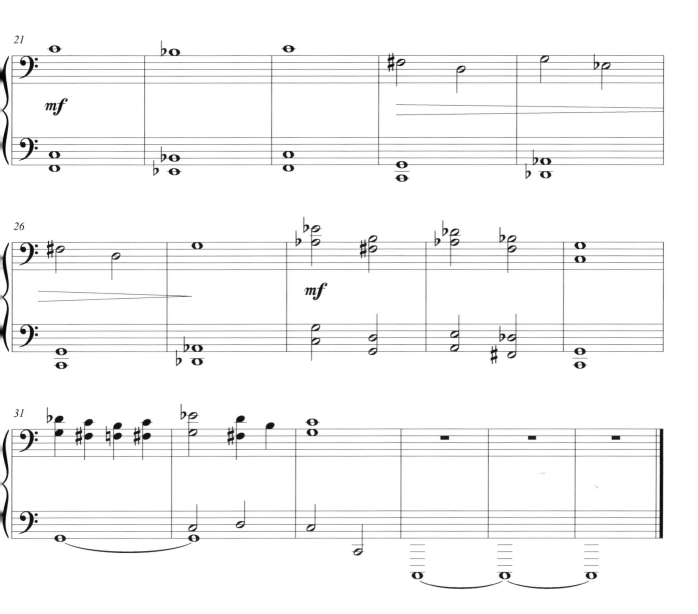

Watch the YouTube video of Jerald playing this by visiting his YouTube page: youtube. com/jeraldsimon. It is one of the "Cool Songs" videos under the "Ghosts and Goblins and Freaks and Ghouls by Jerald Simon" playlist. You may also type in "Darkness by Jerald Simon" in the YouTube search box to find the video as well.

Skill - Students learn C minor pentascale (C D E flat F and G) and also the first five intervals from the C minor pentascale (prime 1st interval, Major 2nd interval, minor 3rd interval, Perfect 4th, and Perfect 5th intervals as well.

JERALD SIMON

SPOOK

Watch the YouTube video of Jerald playing this by visiting his YouTube page: youtube.com/
jeraldsimon. It is one of the "Cool Songs" videos under the "Ghosts and Goblins and Freaks
and Ghouls by Jerald Simon" playlist. You may also type in "Spook by Jerald Simon" in the
YouTube search box to find the video as well.

Haunted

Skill - Accidentals galore. There are a lot of accidentals that aren't in the key of C Major. That's kind of scar
if you don't watch what you are doing!

JERALD SIMON

Are You Scared Yet? (M.M. ♩ = c. 100)

Haunted

Watch the YouTube video of Jerald playing this by visiting his YouTube page: youtube.com/jeraldsimon. It is one of the "Cool Songs" videos under the "Ghosts and Goblins and Freaks and Ghouls by Jerald Simon" playlist. You may also type in "Haunted by Jerald Simon" in the YouTube search box to find the video as well.

Ghosts & Goblins & Freaks & Ghouls

This fun "cool song" was created for a halloween haunting! Have FUN! playing this poisenous piano piece. Watch out for the tricky right and left hand patterns. It's a scary sound beginning in measure 18. Since the notes are clumped together, the note names have been written out in measures 18 and 26. This is a perfect piece to learn to create a scary piano solo of your own. Try using the clumped chords in measure 18 to create a frigtening and freaky composition of your own. Don't get scared now!

JERALD SIMON

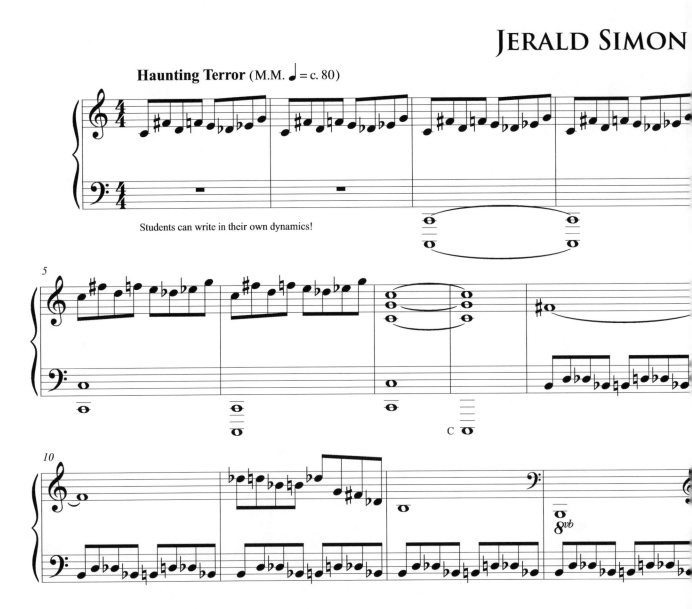

Ghosts & Goblins & Freaks & Ghouls

Fortress of FEAR

Skill - Accidentals galore. There are a lot of accidentals that aren't in the key of C Major. In this piece we ar
also working on the chromatic scale. That's kind of scary if you don't watch what you are doing!

JERALD SIMON

Fortress of FEAR

Place your right arm down and
wherever it lands, it sounds great!
(at least with this scary piece)

(Right Arm)

(Right Arm)

(Right Arm)

Under Siege

This fun "cool song" is in the key of E minor - the relative minor to G major. I wanted to create a piece that would be more of a contemporary classical style for the piano part, while the background instrument: where modern and pop sounding. The left hand is primarily playing triads (three note chords), and octave intervals. The fun part about this piece is that the right hand crosses the left hand. Have fun playing this!

Watch the YouTube video of Jerald playing this by visiting his YouTube page: youtube.com/jeraldsimon. I is one of the "Cool Songs" videos under the "Platinum by Jerald Simon" playlist.

JERALD SIMON

UNDER SIEGE

A Music Mentor? (written by Jerald Simon on Oct. 29th, 2008)

It may seem odd, but it's not enough to be a teacher or an educator. In and of itself, teaching and educating inspirational and praiseworthy (we might even say note-worthy), but to effectively teach, educate, and perpe uate the desire to continually progress and improve, requires mentoring - both as a mentor and in being men tored by mentors of our own. We must continually learn and grow and not only teach, but we must be taug on a regular and consistent basis.

There is an interesting parallel between mentoring and success. Teaching can be done (and somewhat effectiv ly) without much mentoring, but learning and wanting to continually progress cannot exist without mentorin

We are all mentors! As a mentor, we must do everything with the attitude of leading by example. Tellin someone to do something we personally would not do or have not done in a while or at all, but think is good idea for those we mentor is a false form of teaching and mentoring. We are telling those we mentor th we want them to do as we say and not as we do. We convey the attitude that we may have learned this skill performed this technique when we were younger, but no longer feel the need to continue because we perfect demonstrate that we are textbook teachers in word only and not doers (this of course does not apply if we a not physically capable of doing what we did when we were younger because of physical limitations with o bodies).

As mentors, we must use every means available – both conventional and non-conventional – to make a diffe ence in the lives of the individuals we mentor. We must be examples and role models not only in what we sa but also in what we do. We must push those we mentor to continually be better, do more, learn more, try mor and even fail more (yes, I said fail more).

People are too afraid of failure. It prohibits them from progressing because the fear of failure prevents the from being productive. It instigates procrastination because, as a whole, we would rather continually put o what we fear doing and instead do nothing to avoid failure or to appear to be less than perfect in any area. V value our performance and fear giving a less than perfect performance regardless of what it is, or is not. V must understand that failure is merely a stepping stone to success – a way to turn our individual failures in personal strengths.

As mentors we must also not be afraid to show those we mentor our weaknesses and our limitations. We mu not convey the perception of perfection because even though we mentor others, we are not true mentors unle we are learning and being mentored by our own mentors in the process. We must continue to look to othe for guidance.

Being a mentor is life changing. Those who have been mentored realize the importance of mentoring. We mu think of ourselves as a teacher regardless of what we teach. A coach views himself or herself as someone wl coaches an individual or a team to focus on the main objective (playing the game and winning). As mento we help those we mentor focus on playing the game of life. We may use our talent or mastery of a particul instrument as a means to help them, but we are giving them much more than a musical talent. We may s we are piano teachers, voice teachers, violin teachers, guitar teachers, and any other kind of teacher availab but we do not merely teach them how to play an instrument. We teach discipline, self mastery, practice habi conditioning, dedication, goal setting and achieving, determination, confidence, strength training, optimisr perseverance, self worth, and every other worthy and uplifting attitude and aptitude. We are helping them the very best they can be. We use an instrument as our vehicle to help them master a skill, develop a talent, a get in touch with their musical side. Our music motivates us as much as it motivates those around us.

A Few Additional Ideas for Piano Teachers and Parents of Piano Students

You can visit this link to read the original blog post from which this presentation was created: (https://www.musicmotivation.com/blog/don-t-teach-music-theory-unless-you-teach-the-practical-application).

In the blog post, I talked specifically about 10 steps to begin teaching the practical application of music theory so students know their theory inside and out. I thought I would share the 10 steps here from the blog post:

Before any piano student plays their piece, I believe they should be able to do the following (this is what I try to have my students do with their music):

1. Tell their music teacher the key signature and time signature.

2. Identify all of the sharps or flats in the key signature.

3. Play all of the intervals created from the major key signature of the piece they are playing - this is more for piano students and possibly guitar students, as many instruments only allow one note at a time. If the student is younger or new to their instrument, they can play the intervals created from the pentascales or five note scales created from the first five notes of the major or minor scales.

4. Play through the major scale of the key signature of the piece at least 1-2 octaves up and down the piano (parallel and or contrary motion). If the student is younger or new to their instrument, as stated before, they can play the pentascales, or five note scales created from the first five notes of the major or minor scales.

5. Play what I refer to as the "Essential Piano Exercises" from each key signature. (In the blog post I show an example from the key of C major from my book "Essential Piano Exercises" - Intervals, Scales, and Chords in all Keys and in all Inversions - a 288 page book with all intervals, scales, and simple triads and 6th and 7th chords in all keys and inversions).

These are the other 5 steps:

Once a student can do the above five essential "getting started steps" in any given key signature (and many times I will do the following steps even if they can't do the above steps in every key signature), I then challenge them to do the following five essential "music theory application steps."

1. Once the student has learned and perfected the piece, ask him or her to take the song up half a step and down half a step. In the beginning, this is a good start. Later on, when they are better able to do so, have the student play the piece in any key signature. Start with simple pieces like "Mary Had a Little Lamb" and "Twinkle, Twinkle, Little Star." Have the students try playing these in all key signatures.

2. Ask the student to come up with at least 5-10 variations or arrangements of their piece.

3. Ask the student to compose 3 or 4 motifs (or single melodic line or phrase), and then put them together. This can be the beginning of creating a simple piece. I have students begin using scales and skipping notes here and there. We then have them take a simple pattern created from the notes of the major scale (1 2 3 4 5 6 7 8).

4. Ask the student to "Play a Rainbow." When I say this to students, I then begin to ask them to "play" anything. I may say: "Play me a shadow," "Play me a swing set," or "Play me a thunderstorm," "Play me a puddle, a rock, a tree, a meadow, a light, etc.". The sky is the limit. I first begin with tangible objects and eventually move on to intangible ideas and concepts: "Play me loneliness," "Play me disturbed, agitated, angered, humbled, pensive, etc.". Again, the sky is the limit. It is wonderful to see what students can create, even if they don't know all the rules of composition or terminology. Everyone has music within them.

5. I have students begin notating their music. I enjoy and prefer Finale, but that is because I have used it for so long and am familiar with it. There are many great programs available. After we have their music put down on paper, I then export the music from Finale as a midi file and open the midi file in Logic Pro. We then begin having them add additional instruments so they can create background tracks (this is how I create all of my weekly "**Cool Songs**" from my **COOL SONGS Series** (you can learn more about my COOL SONGS Series at this link: https://musicmotivation.com/coolsongs/). The students then have a PDF copy of their composition and an MP3 "minus track" to accompany them as they play. Talk about music motivation!

These are the books included in the COOL SONGS Series: https://musicmotivation.com/coolsongs/ -

The Apprentice Stage - The Maestro Stage - The Virtuoso Stage

COOL SONGS for COOL KIDS (Primer Level) by Jerald Simon
COOL SONGS for COOL KIDS (book 1) by Jerald Simon
COOL SONGS for COOL KIDS (book 2) by Jerald Simon
COOL SONGS for COOL KIDS (book 3) by Jerald Simon
COOL SONGS that ROCK! (book 1) by Jerald Simon
COOL SONGS that ROCK! (book 2) by Jerald Simon

Join the **Essential Piano Exercises Course** by Jerald Simon
https://www.essentialpianoexercises.com

Gain lifetime access to the PDF books listed below (which also includes video piano lesson tutorials where Jerald Simon demonstrates examples from the books and gives piano pointers, tips to try, and the practical application of music theory). Jerald demonstrates how to use the music theory to arrange and compose music of your own!

This course features pre-recorded video lessons so you can watch and learn how to play the piano at your convenience. You choose when and where you learn to play the piano.

Join the **Essential Piano Exercises Course** and receive the following PDF books along with access to the monthly video lesson taught by Jerald Simon for a one time payment of $199.95.

youtube.com/jeraldsimon

I upload new videos on Wednesdays, and Fridays on my YouTube channel, **youtube.com/jeraldsimon**. I have a few different playlists filled with great content for beginning - advanced piano students. The videos are geared for everyone from brand new piano students to music majors, professional pianists, and piano teachers of all skill levels.

There are three main playlists for my **free on-line piano lessons.** I do offer in person piano lessons, Zoom/FaceTime piano lessons, and step by step piano lesson packages you can purchase and watch at home (https://www.musicmotivation.com/pianolessons), but the ones listed below are FREE to everyone who subscribes to my YouTube channel:

1. **PIANO FUNdamentals** (emphasis on the word FUN!)
2. **5 Minute Piano Lessons with Jerald Simon** (sponsored by Music Motivation®)
3. **Theory Tip Tuesday Piano Lessons**

I frequently release new videos. Some are piano lessons, and others are filmed recordings of workshops, masterclasses, or concerts. I also have these additional types of videos on my YouTube channel:

a. **Meditation/Relaxation Music Composed by Jerald Simon**
b. **Hymn Arrangements by Jerald Simon**
c. **Motivational Messages by Jerald Simon**
d. **Motivational Poetry by Jerald Simon**
e. **Theory Tip Tuesday (FREE Weekly Piano Lesson Videos) by Jerald Simon**
f. **Cool Songs by Jerald Simon (musicmotivation.com/coolsongs)**
g. **Assemblies, Workshops, Firesides, and more...**

Let me know if you have a tutorial you'd like me to come out with to better help you learn the piano. I'm happy to help in any way I can and love hearing feedback from others about what they personally are looking for in piano lesson videos to help them learn to play the piano better. I primarily focus on music theory, improvisation/arranging, and composition. I refer to these as **THEORY THERAPY, INNOVATIVE IMPROVISATION, and CREATIVE COMPOSITION**.

I have also produced hundreds of COOL SONGS that teach students music theory the fun way. If you'd like to learn more about the COOL SONGS, that I composed to motivate my own piano students, or if you would like to purchase the COOL SONGS series featuring the music/books, simply visit musicmotivation.com/coolsongs to be taken to the page on my website that explains a little more about the COOL SONGS. You can also watch piano video tutorial lessons featuring 85 of the 200 + COOL SONGS (youtube.com/jeraldsimon). Let me know what you think. I'd love your feedback about the music. It helps me as I compose more COOL SONGS to motivate more piano students. I'm excited to have you watch my free video piano lessons on YouTube.com/jeraldsimon.

Learn more about
JERALD SIMON

Visit https://www.musicmotivation.com/jeraldsimon

"My purpose and mission in life is to motivate myself and others through my music and writing, to help others find their purpose and mission in life, and to teach values and encourage everyone everywhere to do and be their best." - Jerald Simon

First and foremost, Jerald is a husband to his beautiful wife, Zanny, and a father to his wonderful children. Jerald Simon is the founder of **Music Motivation®** (musicmotivation.com), a company he formed to provide music instruction through workshops, giving speeches and seminars, concerts and performances in the field of music and motivation. He is a composer, author, poet, and Music Mentor/piano teacher (primarily focusing his piano teaching on music theory, improvisation, composition, and arranging). Jerald loves spending time with his wife, Zanny, and their children. In addition, he loves music, teaching, speaking, performing, playing sports, exercising, reading, writing poetry and self help books, and gardening.

Jerald Simon is the founder of **Music Motivation®** and focuses on helping piano students and piano teachers learn music theory, improvisation, and composition. He refers to these areas as: **Theory Therapy™, Innovative Improvisation™, and Creative Composition™.** Simon is an author and composer and has written 30 music books featuring almost 300 original compositions, 15 albums (you can listen to Jerald's music on Pandora, Spotify, iTunes, Amazon, and all online music stations. Jerald's books and CDs are also available from Amazon, Wal-Mart.com, Barnes and Noble and all major retail outlets). He has published three motivational poetry books featuring over 400 original poems (poetrythatmotivates.com), and is the creator of the best-selling **Cool Songs Series** (musicmotivation.com/coolsongs), the best-selling **Essential Piano Exercises Series** (essentialpianoexercises.com) and Essential Piano Lessons for piano students (essentialpianolessons.com). He has also created **Essential Piano Teachers** for piano teachers (essentialpianoteachers.com). You can watch Jerald's videos on his YouTube channel at: youtube.com/jeraldsimon. Listen to Jerald's music on all streaming sites and his podcast, **Music, Motivation, and More – The Positivity Podcast** with Jerald Simon on all podcast platforms.

In 2008, Jerald began creating his Cool Songs to help teach music theory – the FUN way, by putting FUN back into theory FUNdamentals. Jerald has also filmed hundreds of piano lesson video tutorials on his YouTube page (youtube.com/jeraldsimon). In addition to music books and albums, he is the author/poet of **"The As If Principle"** (motivational poetry), and the books **"Perceptions, Parables, and Pointers," "Motivation in a Minute,"** and **"Who Are You?"**.

SPECIALTIES:

Composer, Author, Poet, Music Mentor, Piano Teacher (jazz, music theory, improvisation, composition, arranging, etc.), Motivational Speaker, and Life Coach. Visit **https://www.musicmotivation.com/**, to book Jerald as a speaker/performer. Visit **https://www.musicmotivation.com/** to print off FREE piano resources for piano teachers and piano students.

Book me to speak/perform for your group or for a concert or performance:

jeraldsimon@musicmotivation.com - **(801)644-0540** - https://www.musicmotivation.com/

Made in the USA
Las Vegas, NV
22 September 2023

77958886R00020